When I Grow Up, I'll Be A 'Nole!

Requests for permission to make copies of any part of the work should be submitted online at info@mascotbooks.com or mailed to Mascot Books, 560 Herndon Parkway #120, Herndon, VA 20170

PRT0811A

Printed in the United States.

ISBN-13: 978-1-936319-59-6
ISBN-10: 1-936319-59-4

www.mascotbooks.com

To J.D. - A FUTURE 'NOLE!

To all future 'Noles, wherever you may be.

-Amy Hammond

WHEN I GROW UP, I'll BE A 'NOLE!

Amy Hammond
illustrated by **Charr Floyd**

When I grow up, I'll be a 'Nole!

In these pages, I'll tell you why.

I'm garnet and gold from my head to my feet –

F-S-U! is my battle cry.

I've always believed that tomahawks rule.

They slice Gator chomps every time.

I know I'll soon be headed to school

past the *Welcome to Tallahassee* sign.

Someday my drum will rally our fans;

I'll march with war paint and pride.

I may even be the receiving star

and catch winning touchdowns in stride.

When gameday arrives, I'll paint my face gold.

My allegiance will shine in the crowd.

All Doak Campbell Stadium will notice my zeal

And heckle and shout ever loud.

When I grow up, at races I'll cheer.

You'll find me at Mike Long Track.

Our runners will hear me and sprint to the tape with all other schools in the back.

When I grow up, I'll be a success!

In Strozier Library, I'll cram for tests.

I'll handle it all, though my plate will be full –

it's all just a part of being a 'Nole.

When I grow up, I'll be homecoming's star
At a Pow Wow like none seen before.

GO SEMINOLES! I'll lead the cheer -
the crowd will all stand up and roar.

At Florida State, I'll do it all -

walk the tightrope after acing my class.

At FSU, you can be anything -

and all while having a blast!

High-fives to you, my fellow 'Noles!

The choice we made was wise.

Our education will be grand –
and that's no big surprise.

News flash to you kids out there:

The Seminoles are great!

Those other schools are just all right.

Join me at Florida State!

Florida State, Florida State,

Florida State! Woo!

I'll shout it 'till I'm blue!

It's my favorite university –

the best one – and that's true!

To all of you students, alumni and fans

who dream dreams in garnet and gold -

When I grow up, I'll be a 'Nole!

My future is now foretold.

About the author

Amy Hammond lives in St. Petersburg
with her husband, son and daughter. She
thinks every child should grow up setting
their sights on college greatness.